A Big Box of Bananas

by Jay Dale
illustrated by Nick Diggory

One day, Mr Lee looked
in a big box of bananas.

"Help! Help!" cried Mr Lee.
He ran out of the shop
and down the street.

"Mr Lee!" said Mrs Long.
"Where are you going?"

"Help! Help!" cried Mr Lee.
"It came out of
my box of bananas!
It was brown!
It was hairy,
and it was very, very scary!"

5

"Mr Lee," said Mrs Long.
"Was it a hairy brown dog?"

"No!" said Mr Lee.

"It was NOT a hairy brown dog."

"Mr Lee," said Mrs Long.
"Was it a hairy brown cat?"

"No!" said Mr Lee.

"It was NOT a hairy brown cat."

"Come with me," said Mrs Long.
"Let's look in your
big box of bananas."
And off she went!

"Let's look in your
big box of bananas,"
said Mrs Long.
"I can see ten yellow bananas.
They are not brown!
They are not hairy,
and they are NOT
very, very scary!"

"**HELP!**" cried Mr Lee.

A hairy brown spider
came out of the box.

"**HELP!**" cried Mrs Long.

They ran out of the shop and down the street.
And the spider ran, too!